Spot the Difference:
Fire Trucks

Each page has two fire truck themed pictures with five differences.
Can you find them all?

Some are easy, most are difficult.
Solutions are in the back of the book.

Join the Spot the Difference group to get notified when new books are published.
I also send out unique puzzles for members.

https://puzzle.pictures

www.london-fire.gov.uk
FIRE
LFB
LONDON FIRE BRIGADE
SOHO
DPL1274
241
BE SAFE & SOUND
08000 28 44 28

SV-45-38
SV-45-38

Air Pro, Inc.
A12
E111

RESCUE
MOREHEAD
FIRE DEPT.
ENGINE NO
10
Pierce
RESCUE
MOREHEAD
FIRE DEPT.
ENGINE NO
10
Pierce

ENGINE 3613
ENGINE 3613

KEEP BACK 300 FT.
KEEP BACK 300 FT.

BOSTON
20

CAPTAIN
MSA

1/65-2
FEUERWEHR
Arocs
WLF 2
MZ RI 1045

VG Sprendlingen-Gensingen
112
7-72-1
FEUERWEHR
72
MZ SG 1202

VG Sprendlingen-Gensingen
112
7-72-1
FEUERWEHR
72
MZ SG 1202

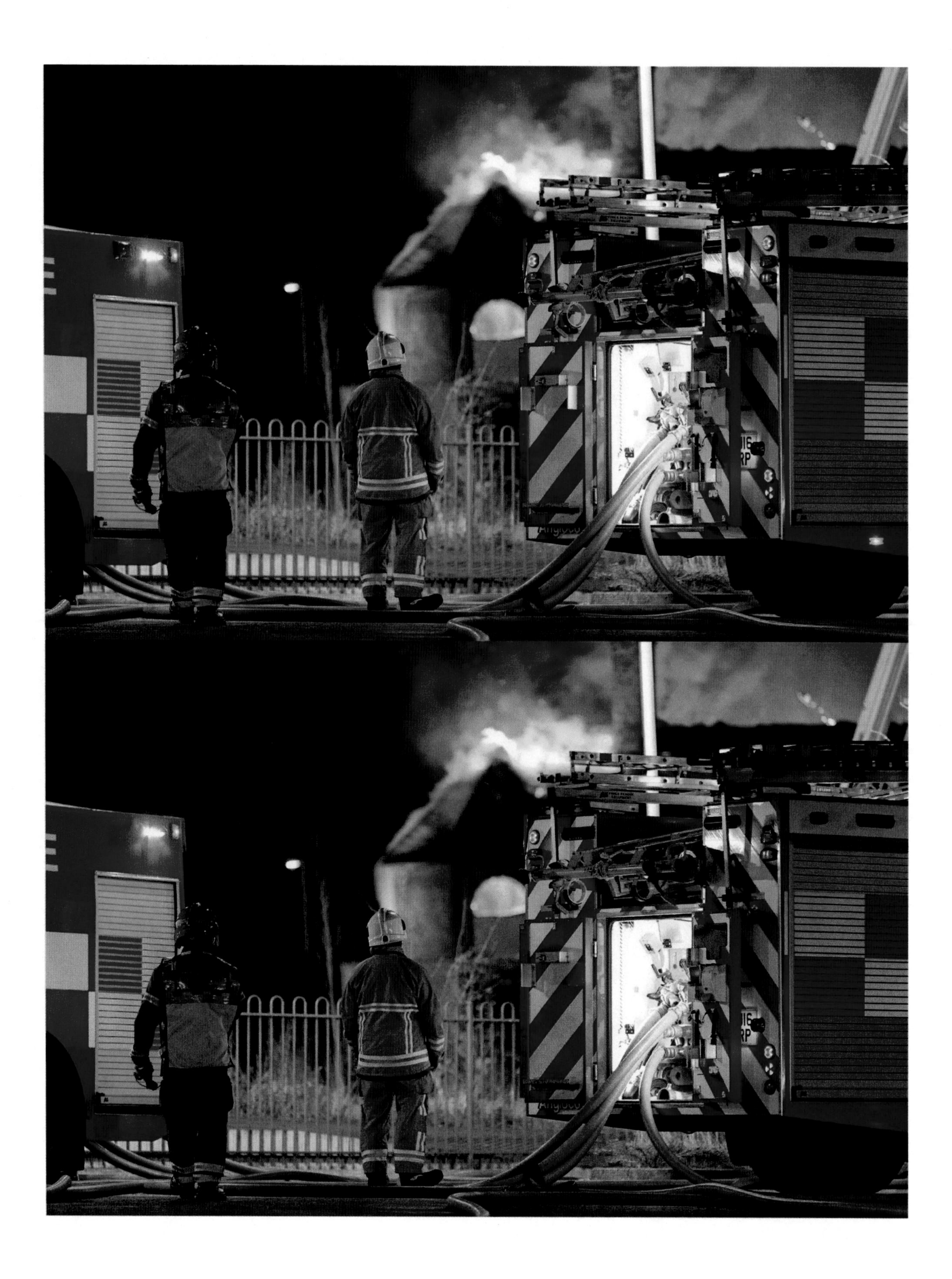

R480
ZS 1081L
STRAZ

R480
ZS 1081L
ZS 1081L

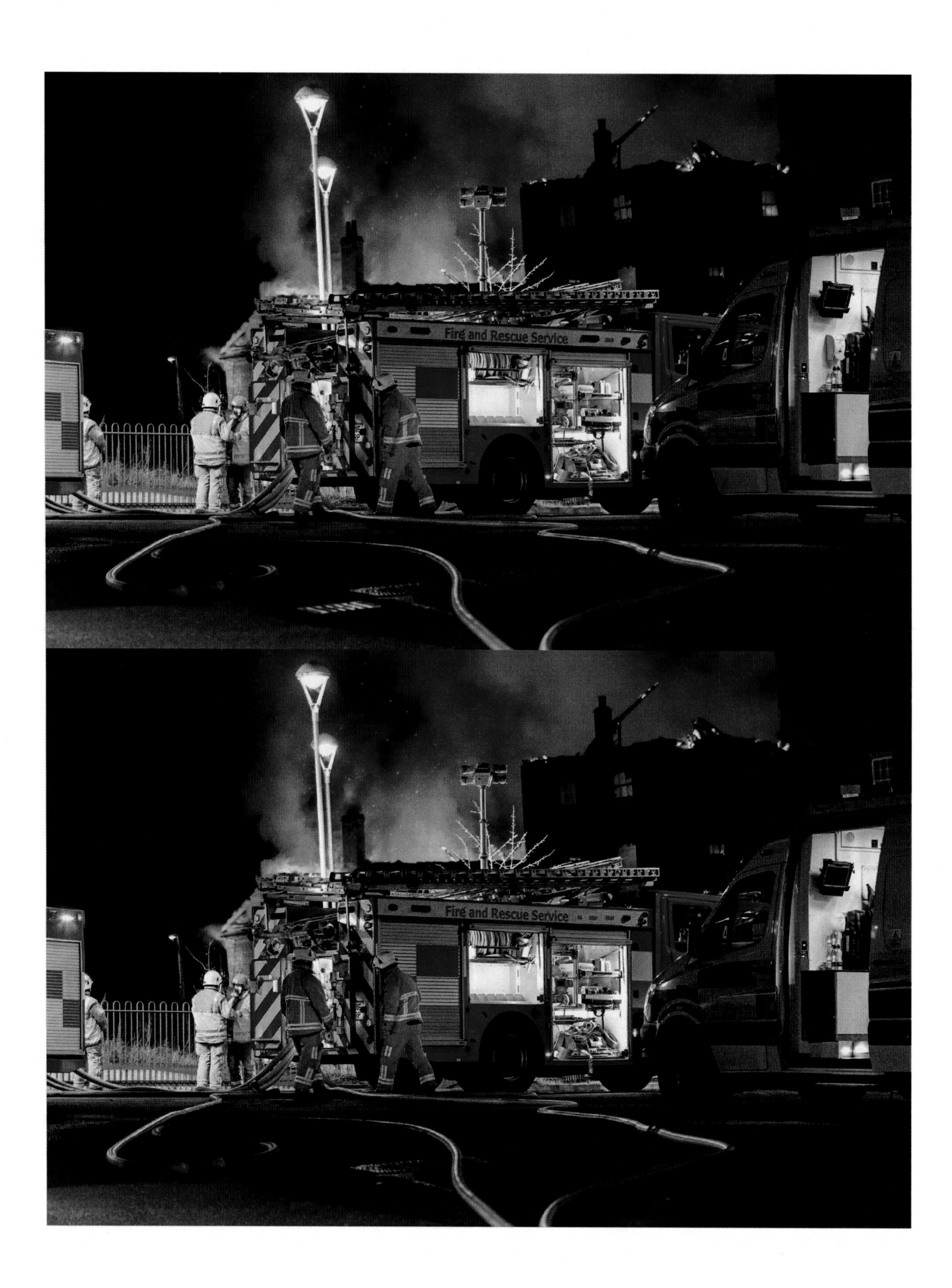
Fire and Rescue Service
Fire and Rescue Service

PREJMER
POMPIERI
PREJMER-BV 199
PREJMER
POMPIERI
PREJMER-BV 199

Pierce
Pierce

Striker

DE CYMRU
DE CYMRU

SOUTH WALES

SOUTH WALES

minerva
SECOURS

SUNNY SIDE
55
The Double Nickel
SUNNY SIDE
55
The Double Nickel

WOOD
SHED
FIRE DEPT.
ENGINE

DS 2
SCANIA
SDS
94D
HX53 WNV
260

WEST SUSSEX FIRE & RESCUE SERVICE
MAN
WEST SUSSEX FIRE & RESCUE SERVICE
MAN

WORKING
ON FIRE
FIRE 1
TRANSPEC
WORKING
ON FIRE
FIRE 1
TRANSPEC

Wards
SUMMIT
HOSE
TARENTUM
E 282
282
SUTPHEN
SUMMIT
HOSE

112
BFG 992
ZLN 459

SUNNY SIDE
HOUSTON
FIRE
55

FIRE
S150
KEEP BACK 150m

FIRE DEPT.
FIRE

ATASCOCITA
TW 19
WWW.AVFD.COM
ATASCOCITA
TW 19
WWW.AVFD.COM

SPRING
SCAFFOLDING LLC
THE MID
TOWN MOB
F.D.
N.Y.
65

HONOLULU
FIRE DEPT.
ENGINE
15
HAU'ULA
HONOLULU
FIRE
DEPARTMENT
911

T. F. D.
Nº27

T. F. T.
Nº27

B.A. ENTRY CONTROL BOARD
BA ANCILLARIES
BA BOARD

ENGINE 2
BOOTHBAY
FIRE DEPARTMENT

ENGINE 1

3
F.D
N.Y.
RECON

BEARDMORE
FIRE DEPT
BEARDMORE
FIRE

E 43
HARRISBURG
FIRE & RESCUE
DIAL 911

SAN FRANCISCO
E 13
E13

WE SUPPORT
OUR TROOPS
HOUSTON
RL 20
MAGNOLIA PARK
754-847
WE SUPPORT
OUR TROOPS
HOUSTON
RL 20
MAGNOLIA PARK
754-847

Hilton
HOUSTON FIRE
DEPARTMENT
MC-8
TEXAS
111 1627

HOUSTON LADDER 7
7
24
HOUSTON LADDER 7
7
24

Orange
reade
F.D.N.Y.
26
www.nyc.gov/fdny
N.Y.
F.D.

WORKING
ON FIRE
FT34
150E24
ANCO

Tatra
4U5 3740
Tatra
4U5 3740

FIRE
SV-45-38
RESCUE
KEEP BACK 300 FT
BOSTON
MSA

FEUERWEHR
112
FEUERWEHR
ZS 1081L
ZS 1081L
PREJMER
POMPIER

WOOD
SHED
Double Nickel
SCANIA
94D
HX53 WNV
260

MAN
FIRE 1
Wards
SUMMIT HOSE
TARENTUM
E 282
SUNNY SIDE
HOUSTON
FIRE
55
FIRE

ATASCOCITA
TW 19
FIRE

3
FD NY
RECON
BEARDMORE
FIRE DEPT
BEARDMORE
FIRE DEPT
E 13
E 13
HOUSTON
MAGNOLIA PARK
MC-8
HOUSTON LADDER

26
FT34
WORKING
ON FIRE
4U6 3740

Made in United States
Orlando, FL
10 April 2023